BERtie'S
UnCIe BaSiL

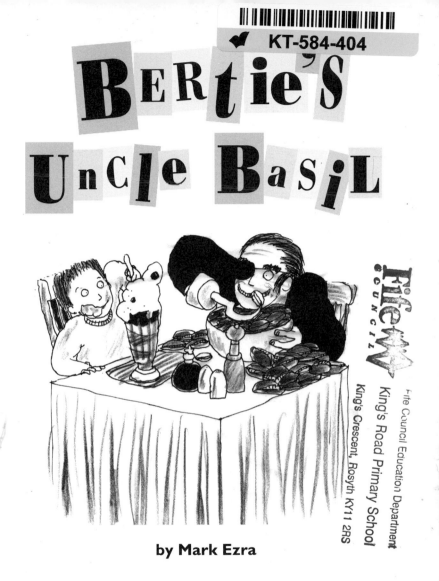

by Mark Ezra

Illustrated by Stephen Lewis

LONGMAN

The cast

Bertie Harding, a boy aged around 10

Mum (Mrs Harding)

Uncle Basil, a man of many parts (and many disguises)

Restaurant manager

Sir Gilbert Foskett-Pume, a nasty old man with a monocle and a moustache

Tarquin, his equally nasty nephew

Harry, doorman at the House of Lords

Railway guards 1 and 2

Cynthia Splatt, a wicked woman

Angela Harte, a beautiful woman with a heart of gold

Solicitor

'**Narrator**' – someone to read the stage directions which are set in italic type like this: *Bertie has his back to the audience ...*

Scene 1

Bertie's home

Bertie has his back to the audience and is hoovering the carpet. He is wearing a pinny and a headscarf.

Mum   *(off)* Bertie! Bertie! BERTIE!

Bertie switches off the vacuum cleaner and turns round, looking thoroughly fed up.

Bertie   What is it now, Mum?

Mum   *(off)* Are you doing the hoovering, like I asked?

Bertie   *(sighing)* Yes Mum.

Mum   *(off)* Can you do it quietly? I've got a headache.

Bertie   *(aside)* Quietly? *(to Mum)* I'm just finishing now.

He makes a whistling noise, in imitation of the vacuum cleaner. He puts the cleaner away, but the long flex tentacle wraps around his neck, almost strangling him. He beats it back and closes the door.

Finished!

Mum	*(entering)* Now go and make some tea.
Bertie	Oh, Mum!
Mum	You haven't got yourself dirty, have you?
Bertie	No, Mum.

Bertie pulls off the pinny and tears off his scarf with relief.

	Mum, can't I have *any* friends round?
Mum	Certainly not. I don't want them messing up the house.
Bertie	But it's my birthday!
Mum	I don't want you mixing with the wrong sort of people.
Bertie	What *are* the "wrong sort of people"?
Mum	You'll know them when you see them. Oh, I almost forgot. Here's your birthday present.

She hands him a small, cheaply wrapped package.

Bertie	Thank you.

Bertie opens the package and holds up a small, dark object.

Bertie	What is it?
Mum	A sock.
Bertie	Shouldn't there be a pair?
Mum	I'm giving you the other half at Christmas.
Bertie	I can't wait.

There is a loud KNOCK on the door.

| **Mum** | Who can that be? |

Bertie goes out. Mum answers the door. An enormous man steps in – an eye patch on one eye, his right hand stuffed in his pocket.

Basil	Good morning, Mrs Harding. I am Bertie's long-lost Uncle Basil.
Mum	Long-lost? Who lost you?
Basil	My brother, your husband.
Mum	Well *I* lost my husband.
Basil	I'm so sorry to hear that.
Mum	Took him to the supermarket one day and when I turned round, he was gone.
Basil	Lucky man. I mean, what a tragedy. I've come to take Bertie out for his birthday.

Mum	I don't let Bertie go out with just anyone. How do I know you are who you say you are?
Basil	Very sensible to take precautions, Madam. You can't trust anybody these days. Here's my driving licence. Is that proof enough?
Mum	Basil Harding … yes, now I look at you, I can see the resemblance.
Basil	Call the boy in. I expect you're finding him quite a handful.
Mum	I am, I am. Ever since that brother of yours disappeared, I've been at my wits' end. Bertie's costing me a fortune in washing powder.
Basil	Messy things, boys.
Mum	Bertie! You've got a visitor.

Bertie comes in.

Basil	Hello, Bertie.
Mum	Say hello to your Uncle Basil.

Bertie holds out his hand.

Bertie	Hello, Uncle Basil.

Basil holds out his right hand. Only it isn't a hand. It's a shiny black hook!

Bertie   *(aside)* He's a pirate!

Basil   Don't you worry, Mrs Harding. I'll take good care of him. Come on, Bertie.

Basil goes out.

Bertie   Mum, he's a pirate! He's going to kidnap me and hold me for ransom!

Mum   Nonsense!

Bertie   That's what pirates do!

Basil reappears, hooks Bertie's arm and guides him out.

Basil   Don't worry, Mrs Harding. I'll take good care of him.

Scene 2

A famous restaurant

Basil and Bertie enter.

Basil   You'll like this restaurant. The food is absolutely scrumptious.

Bertie   *(aside)* What an old dinosaur! This doesn't look like much of a treat.

Manager   I'm sorry sir, but that boy cannot enter the restaurant without a tie.

Basil   That's all right, he can have yours.

Bertie   He's pulled off the Manager's bow tie!

Basil   Look at that! A cheap clip on. What is this place coming to? Here you are, Bertie – let's clip this on to your shirt.

Bertie   *(aside)* What a bully!

Basil   We'll sit there.

Manager   I'm sorry sir. That table is reserved for Sir Gilbert Foskett-Pume.

Basil   Then Sir Gilbert's going to be disappointed, isn't he? We got here first. What time is his reservation?

Manager	One o'clock, sir.
Basil	It's quarter past one now. Old Sir Gilbert should have got here on time. Bad manners to be late.
Manager	But the table is *booked*.

Basil slips his hook under the manager's collar.

Basil	Then *un*book it!
Bertie	*(aside)* That hook's dangerous!
Manager	*(nervously)* Your table's ready, sir.
Basil	Don't bother to bring me the menu. I know what I want.
Manager	Of course, sir.

The Manager gives Bertie a menu. He looks at it in dismay.

Bertie	It's all in French!
Basil	I'll have a dozen oysters, then a dozen garlicky snails, then another dozen oysters …
Bertie	Yuck!
Basil	And then I'll have the grilled turbot and half a bottle of your finest white wine.

Manager	Of course, sir. And the boy?
Bertie	*(small voice)* I don't want any slimy oysters or slippery snails.
Basil	Bring him a Knickerbocker Glory for starters, a treacle tart with custard for his main course, and a fruit trifle for pudding. And leave a large bottle of Coke on the table.
Manager	Very good, sir.

The Manager goes off. Bertie brightens up.

Basil	Did I order what you wanted?
Bertie	Yes. They're all my favourites. I'm never allowed to eat them at home. Mum says they're not good for me.
Basil	They were my favourites when I was a boy. You deserve a treat on your birthday.
Bertie	Last year Mum made me do my homework and sent me up to bed early.
Basil	I was up Mount Everest at the time, searching for yetis.
Bertie	What's a yeti?
Basil	The abominable snowman.

Bertie	Did you find one?
Basil	More than one. But that's another story.
Manager	Your oysters, sir … Your Knickerbocker Glory … sir.
Basil	Delicious. They're still alive, you know. You squeeze a few drops of lemon on them and they curl up at the edges.
Bertie	Poor things!

Basil   And then it's down the hatch in one
            smooth, guzzling gulp. Mmm, delicious!
            Want one?

Bertie   No way!

Basil   All the more for me, then.

*Basil burps. Bertie eats some Knickerbocker Glory
and burps back.*

Basil   That's the ticket!

*Sir Gilbert Fosket-Pume enters with his young
nephew, Tarquin.*

Gilbert   Who's that sitting at my table?

Tarquin   Who's that eating my lunch?

Basil   Must be Goldilocks.

Manager   I have a table for you over here, Sir Gilbert.

Basil   Study those two carefully, Bertie. It's
            very important you remember everything
            about them. It could be a matter of life
            and death.

Gilbert   Where's the menu?

Manager   On its way, sir.

Gilbert   Got legs, has it?

Manager   I'll just go and get it.

As the Manager goes, Sir Gilbert sticks out his leg, tripping him up. Sir Gilbert laughs wickedly.

Bertie   What a horrible old man!

Basil   That's Sir Gilbert and his nasty nephew, Tarquin. They're a couple of real rotters. Now if you've had a really good look at them, we'll be on our way, because we've got an important mission ahead of us.

Bertie   What sort of mission?

Basil   Can't tell you yet, but I can promise it'll be a pretty exciting adventure.

Scene 3

Outside the House of Lords

Bertie is following Basil along the street.

Bertie   Where are we?

Basil   You'll see in a moment.

Bertie   That's Big Ben!

Basil   Quite right, Bertie. Big Ben and the Houses of Parliament.

Basil suddenly removes his eye patch and hook, revealing a perfectly good hand underneath. He sticks a ginger moustache under his nose.

Bertie   What are you doing?

Basil   I felt in need of a change. Follow me.

Bertie   We can't go in there! They'll throw us out.

Basil   Leave it to me. Forward march!

Doorman   Good afternoon, your Lordship.

Basil   Good afternoon, Harry … Come on Bertie, don't dawdle, boy! For goodness sake let him in, Harry. He's my nephew.

Doorman   Of course, your Lordship.

Bertie   Are you really a lord?

Basil   Is anyone looking? No? Then follow me.

Basil pushes open a door marked "FIRE EXIT". The door swings open and Basil yanks Bertie inside.

Scene 4
The secret hideout

The secret hideout is a beautiful room overlooking the Thames.

Bertie   Where are we? Whose room is this?

Basil   Ours. It used to belong to some old Duke who had it as his private drawing-room, but when he died nobody claimed it, so I took it over.

Bertie   But did they know about it? I mean, it *is* hidden behind a fire exit.

Basil   Brilliant idea, eh? I knocked that up one weekend more than twenty years ago.

Bertie   You mean you've been living here for *twenty years?*

Basil   On and off. I do have other homes, you know.

Bertie   Doesn't anyone get suspicious? You're not a *real* lord, are you?

Basil   You know that, and I know that, but as long as *they* don't know that, nothing needs to change.

Bertie   But what about the guards?

Basil   I don't worry about them. Lots of lords never attend Parliament, so the guards can't possibly know them all. There's a chap in the Orkney Islands, Lord Curmudgeon, of that ilk, who hasn't been seen for forty years. If they question me, I say I'm old Curmudgeon. Nobody can prove that I'm not.

Bertie   Is it legal?

Basil   What's that got to do with it? I'm not hurting anybody. Of course, it's become a bit tricky since they started televising the debates. You can spot me sometimes, snoozing in the back row, if you look hard enough. This is the only place in London where you can get a decent kip without having some busybody trying to move you on. Ah, here we are … this is what we need – a suitcase with a couple of changes of clothes. Now brush your hair and wash your hands. We've got a long journey ahead of us.

Scene 5

A railway carriage and corridor

Basil and Bertie climb into the railway carriage from the platform. A guard stops near them.

Guard 1   All aboard!

He blows his whistle and the train starts to move off.

Bertie   This is a first-class carriage. Do we have first-class tickets?

Basil   We don't have *any* tickets. But we will have. I'll be back in a minute.

He goes out. Bertie looks out of the window. Sir Gilbert enters and quickly "bags" all the seats by placing luggage on them.

Gilbert   Shut that window!

Bertie turns with a jump. Sir Gilbert lights up a cigar.

                You heard me. Shut that window at once!

Bertie shuts the window and tries to find an empty seat. He notices the NO SMOKING sign.

Bertie   This is a no-smoking compartment.

Gilbert   So what? Who's going to make me
                stop? You?

Bertie   May I sit down?

Gilbert   If you can find any space.

*Bertie starts to cough from the smoke and staggers
into the corridor. He bumps into Tarquin who is
carrying a tea-tray.*

Tarquin   You stupid clot! Can't you look where you're going? You've made me spill it. Now I'll have to get some more!

Tarquin grumbles off. Sir Gilbert pushes past Bertie.

Gilbert   Out of the way!

Sir Gilbert enters the toilet as Basil appears.

Bertie   What are you doing?

Basil   Shhh!

He raps hard on the door.

Tickets ! Please show your tickets!

Gilbert   I can't show you my ticket now. It's not convenient.

Basil   I don't see why not. I'm at your convenience, aren't I? Hurry up – I can't wait all day.

Gilbert   All right, all right! I'll pass them under the door. One adult and one child.

Basil   *(to Bertie)* There you are. I told you I'd get us some tickets.

Bertie   But … but isn't that stealing?

| **Basil** | Sir Gilbert knows all about stealing. I promise you, Bertie, it's all in a very good cause. |

They enter the compartment. Basil lifts two cases off the seats and places them in the luggage rack. His fingers flick over the straps of one, but we can't quite see what he has done. The guard appears just as Sir Gilbert takes his seat.

Guard 1	Tickets please. Show all tickets please.
Basil	I don't think I can find them.
Gilbert	No tickets, eh? You'll have to pay a fine.
Basil	Ah, here they are.
Gilbert	Huh!
Guard 1	Very good, sir. And now yours, sir?
Gilbert	What do you mean, mine? I gave them to you just a moment ago!
Guard 1	No you didn't. If you don't hand them over, you'll have to get off.
Gilbert	But I … I … What are you staring at boy? Haven't I seen you somewhere before?
Bertie	I don't think so.

Gilbert   Yes I have. You're the little squirt who took my table in the restaurant. No, on second thoughts that particular little reptile was with a great, fat oaf with a hook. Must be a case of mistaken identity, I suppose.

Guard 1   Come on, I'm putting you off at the next stop.

Gilbert   All right, all right. I'm coming.

He reaches for his luggage as Tarquin comes down the corridor, carrying another tray of tea.

Basil   *(to Bertie)* Hold tight.

Sir Gilbert yanks a case down – unaware that it is tied to the communication cord. The carriage is thrown into violent confusion as the train driver brakes violently. Tarquin hurtles out of sight. Another guard appears.

Guard 2   Who pulled the communication cord? Come on, own up!

Guard 1   He did! He's a right troublemaker!

Guard 2   Right, that's an on-the-spot fine for you! Four hundred pounds!

Gilbert   But … but … all I did was pull down my suitcase. The strap must have got wrapped round the cord, somehow.

Guard 2   Come on, cough up.

Gilbert   Oh, all right. That should take care of it … Tarquin! Oh, where's that useless boy got to?

Tarquin appears, covered in tea and cream buns.

Tarquin   I'm here, uncle.

Gilbert   Come on, you lazy clod. We're getting off this train. *(to Bertie)* And I hope I never have to set eyes on you again.

He throws the door open, steps out of the carriage and drops out of sight with a yell of surprise.

Basil   He should have waited till we'd pulled into the station.

Tarquin follows Gilbert with the luggage.

      Now we've got rid of the opposition, let's get this train going. We've got to move fast. I hope you like dressing up?

Bertie   Dressing up? What do you mean?

Basil   Just you wait and see.

Scene 6

Outside a country mansion

Bertie This is never going to work! I feel stupid dressed as a girl.

Basil *(off)* Nonsense. You're every bit as convincing as I am.

Basil steps out onto the stage dressed as a woman. He looks ridiculous.

Masters of disguise. Now leave the talking to me. We're on very dangerous ground.

Bertie looks down at his feet.

Not there. Here! Now if you thought Sir Gilbert was nasty, wait till you see this horrible creature! Her name is Cynthia Splatt, and she hates boys, so don't give yourself away.

He knocks at the door.

Cynthia Yes? What do you want?

Basil Good morning, madam. We're collecting for charity.

Cynthia I never give to charity. Go away.

Basil	Wait! You'll want to give to this one. It's a completely new charity, and when you hear what it is you'll want to give us lots of money.
Cynthia	What is it then?
Basil	Cruelty to animals.
Cynthia	What's new about that? I've heard of that one.
Basil	Not this one, you haven't. This is *for* cruelty to animals.
Cynthia	*For* cruelty to animals? I've never heard of that one.
Basil	It's new. We've just started it.

Bertie tries to say something but Basil clamps a hand over his protesting mouth.

Cynthia	I like the sound of that. Tell me more.
Basil	We're looking for a suitable patron.
Cynthia	I have more fur coats than anyone I know.
Basil	Then you would be ideal.
Cynthia	What exactly does the patron have to do?

Basil	It's so unspeakable, I can't even begin to tell you.
Cynthia	It sounds right up my street.
Basil	Just sign this piece of paper. We'll fill in the details later.

Cynthia signs her name.

	Thank you.
Cynthia	And here is my first contribution … five pounds.
Bertie	*(squeaky voice)* Here's the collection tin.
Cynthia	Ah, a little gurgle! I like little gurgles. I don't like little boils. Boils are nasty, smelly things. But I love gurgles. I was one myself once, you know.
Basil	Really? I would never have guessed. Well, we must be off finding more members. Is there anyone else in the house?
Cynthia	No, nobody at all.
Basil	Well, goodbye then.
Cynthia	*(shutting the door)* Goodbye.

Bertie	What an evil woman!
Basil	She's the most despicable person I've ever come across. Society *for* cruelty to animals indeed! I'm going to send this money to the Battersea Dogs' Home at once.
Bertie	She's wicked!
Basil	The pits! Is she watching us?
Bertie	No.
Basil	Then come over here.

He leads Bertie to the side of the house. They stop at the foot of some ivy trailing up a trellis.

Bertie	What are we going to do now?
Basil	Now we know the coast is clear, we're going to rescue a damsel in distress.
Bertie	Sounds like a squashed prune.
Basil	*Damsel,* I said, not damson! A lady!
Bertie	Where?
Basil	Up there. How good are you at climbing?

Bertie   I don't know. Mum never lets me climb anything in case I get dirty.

Basil   Silly woman! Boys are *supposed* to be dirty. I've never seen one that wasn't. Here's your chance to find out how good you are. I'll be right behind you.

Scene 7

Inside Cynthia's house

Bertie's face appears at the window. He climbs in, then closes the window behind him. Basil reaches the window, slips and drops out of sight with a yell. A moment later a ladder is propped against the window and Basil reappears with twigs in his hair. Bertie opens the window and helps him in.

Basil   I thought I was done for!

Angela   Hold it right there and don't think you can get away. I've called the police.

Bertie nearly jumps out of his skin as a beautiful woman steps forward.

Basil   Angela!

Angela   Basil! I didn't recognise you in those funny clothes!

Basil   Very comfortable for climbing up the sides of buildings. Bit windy though.

Angela   I knew you'd come for me!

Basil   I would never let you down. Let me introduce my nephew Bertie. Bertie, this is my dear friend, Miss Angela Harte.

Angela   Hello, Bertie.

Bertie   Hello.

Basil   Isn't she lovely?

Bertie   She's beautiful. But why are we here? What's going on?

Basil   That evil woman has got Angela locked up here so that Sir Gilbert can claim her inheritance. If Angela doesn't claim it by six tonight, Sir Gilbert and that cruel woman will get it all.

Cynthia appears at the door with a large key in her hand.

Cynthia   And you can't do a thing about it! I'm locking you in. I checked. There's no charity for cruelty to animals. What a pity! Sir Gilbert will be here soon, and then we will all be rich!

She cackles hysterically as she slams the door and turns the key.

Basil   What terrible overacting!

Bertie   She's locked us in. And she's taken the ladder. And chopped down the ivy!

Angela   She thinks of everything.

Bertie   Now you'll never get your inheritance!

Angela   That's all right, Bertie. At least you
               tried.

Basil   She didn't think of quite everything.

*He opens his jacket to reveal a rope wrapped
around his body.*

               Never know when you might need a bit
               of old rope. Just tie it up here and we'll
               let ourselves down. Angela you wait
               here …

Scene 8

Outside the mansion (again)

Basil and Bertie climb down the rope and reach the ground. Basil ferrets round and finds his suitcase.

Basil   Get out of those clothes and into these. We've just got time if we're quick.

He pulls out another set of clothes and they disappear behind bushes. They reappear, and this time they are dressed like Sir Gilbert and Tarquin. Basil places a monocle in his eye and a moustache under his nose.

Perfect. I would hardly know the difference.

He knocks on the door. Cynthia opens it.

Cynthia   Gilbert!

Basil   Cynthia!

He gives her a big kiss.

Cynthia   I was expecting you an hour ago.

Basil   The train was delayed. Where's Angela?

Cynthia	Locked in her room, like you told me. And there are two strange males locked in there with her. One of them is a dirty, rotten scoundrel …
Basil	I heard he's really quite charming …
Cynthia	With the brain of a worm …
Basil	A man of great intellect …
Cynthia	A nose like a gherkin …
Basil	A most noble profile …
Cynthia	A revolting slugapple …
Basil	The looks of a Greek god …
Cynthia	Are we talking about the same person?
Basil	How would I know? I've never met him. Bert … I mean, Tarquin, fetch Angela down.
Cynthia	But they might escape!
Basil	Don't worry. He's a master of karate – with a brown belt in ju-jitsu and a black belt in origami.
Cynthia	I thought that was paper folding.
Basil	Not the way he does it.

Cynthia gives Bertie the key. He disappears inside the house.

Basil   Have no fear, I promise they won't slip past him.

Cynthia   They'd better not.

Basil   Come on, boy, hurry up.

Bertie reappears with Angela.

Basil   Did they give you any trouble?

Bertie   They're mincemeat. Especially the little one – little runt he was.

Gilbert   *(off)* Come on, we're almost there.

Tarquin   *(off)* Can't we stop and rest? I'm tired.

Sir Gilbert staggers into view, followed by Tarquin.

Gilbert   Cynthia, there you are!

He and Tarquin stop dead, face to face with Basil and Bertie.

                What's Angela doing out? Who the devil are you?

Basil   Sir Gilbert.

Gilbert   But *I'm* Sir Gilbert!

Basil	No you're not. *I am.*
Gilbert	No, *I am.*
Basil	Cynthia, they're imposters.
Gilbert	Oh no, I'm not!
Basil & Bertie	Oh yes you are!
Gilbert & Tarquin	Oh no we're not!
Basil & Bertie	Oh yes you are!
Cynthia	This is beginning to sound like a bad panto.
Basil	Well, we were here first.
Cynthia	Exactly. *(to Gilbert) You* are the imposter, a cheap trickster! How dare you pretend to be Sir Gilbert!
Gilbert	But I *am* Sir Gilbert!
Cynthia	And I bet that moustache is just stuck on!

Basil, Bertie and Angela tiptoe away as Cynthia grabs hold of Sir Gilbert's moustache and tugs hard.

Gilbert	Oww! You stupid woman! Of course I'm the real Sir Gilbert!

Tarquin   They're getting away!

Gilbert   After them!

Tarquin   Oh no, not again!

Scene 9

A solicitor's office

The solicitor is sitting at her desk. She glances up at the clock, which indicates one minute to six. She checks her watch.

Solicitor   What a nice quiet day it's been. I might as well go home.

She is about to close her files when Basil, Bertie and Angela burst into her office.

Good heavens!

Basil   We're just in time.

Bertie   This is Angela Harte –

Angela   And I've come to claim my inheritance.

Solicitor   That is good news.

Angela   Here is my birth certificate.

Basil   And here is a document signed by Cynthia Splatt confessing that she has been holding Angela a prisoner against her will, under the instructions of Sir Gilbert.

Bertie   That's the document that Cynthia
              signed! You are clever, Uncle.

Basil   Yes I am, aren't I?

Solicitor All the papers are in order. All you have
              to do is sign here.

Angela signs. A clock strikes six.

Bertie   Just in time.

Basil   Thank you very much. We must be
              going.

Solicitor So soon? Aren't you going to celebrate?
              A glass of sherry perhaps?

Basil   No time!

*Basil, Bertie and Angela hurry out. The next
moment Sir Gilbert, Cynthia and Tarquin burst
into the room.*

Gilbert   We've come to claim the Harte
              inheritance.

Solicitor Weren't you here just a moment ago?

Gilbert   No, I wasn't. Don't tell me those
              impostors have been here already! I am
              the *real* Sir Gilbert!

Solicitor   Then the police will want to interview you. Apparently you've been holding Miss Angela Harte against her will.

Gilbert   *This* is Angela Harte!

He pushes Cynthia forward. The Solicitor inspects her.

Solicitor   Strange. I thought Miss Harte was a much younger woman. This lady seems quite old.

Gilbert   She's had a hard life. Just you hand over the money, and she can get a facelift.

Solicitor   I'm afraid you're too late. The inheritance has already been claimed by its rightful owner. All the real Miss Harte has to do is go to the bank in the morning and it will all be hers.

Cynthia   We're too late! We've lost everything.

Gilbert   *(softly)* We may still have a chance – if we can stop Angela. Just wait till I catch that meddling oaf and that horrid little boy!

Tarquin sees something out of the window.

Tarquin   There they are!

Gilbert   Come on, after them!

Solicitor   It was so quiet all day, now all this noise. My nerves are quite shaken. I think I'll have that sherry after all.

Scene 10

A famous park

Bertie	Where are we?
Basil	Near my other home.
Bertie	But this is –
Basil	Hampton Court maze, exactly.
Angela	They're close behind.
Basil	Then follow me, quick.

He approaches the ticket kiosk.

Basil	Two adults, one child, please … They're right behind us, come on! Follow the path round to the right. Take the first sharp left, the next right, walk five paces forward and stop. In you go.

He yanks at a yew bush which comes away easily (its roots are in a pot) leaving a gap in the maze hedge. They all step through and Basil replaces the bush behind him. They are in a secret house in the maze. It has sofas and a bed.

Bertie	But where are we?

Basil	My country residence. Now sit still and don't make a sound.
Gilbert	*(off)* This way Tarquin, you useless twit. They're definitely in here somewhere. I saw them come in.
Cynthia	*(off)* I've laddered my tights!
Gilbert	*(off)* Just what we need – a ladder! Then we can see where we're going! Tarquin, where are you?
Tarquin	*(off)* Over here!
Gilbert	*(off)* Where's here?
Tarquin	*(off)* I don't know. I'm lost!
Cynthia	*(off)* So am I!
Gilbert	*(off)* So am I!
All three	*(off)* Help!

Their voices fade away into the distance.

Basil	That's got rid of them.
Bertie	How long have you lived here?
Basil	Years and years. You see, nobody seemed to know about it –

Bertie	So you decided to keep it for yourself. You really are an old scoundrel, Uncle Basil.
Basil	I know.
Angela	But you're a lovable old scoundrel. You probably saved my life.
Basil	You don't need to worry now, Angela. Just turn up at the bank in the morning, show them the papers, and everything will be all right.
Angela	Basil, you've been wonderful. And so have you, Bertie. I don't know how to thank you.
Basil	That's all right, my dear. Ooh, it's been a long day.

Basil falls asleep and starts to snore.

Angela	He's off again. Dreaming.
Bertie	What does he dream about?
Angela	Euphemia.
Bertie	What's Euphemia?
Angela	It's a place most people don't believe in. They think it doesn't exist. But it does. Basil's been there many times in his dreams.

Bertie   Where is it?

Angela   It's a beautiful tropical island. It basks in the sun, but it never gets too hot, because of the cool sea breezes that waft over it. The people who live there are the kindest people in the world. If a weary traveller is washed ashore, they treat him as one of the family, no matter how silly or wicked he or she has been. They forgive all past mistakes. It's a sort of rest home for old scoundrels like Basil. It's just the kind of place where he'd love to spend his last days. Now the coast is clear, it's time we left him to get some sleep. If you're ready, I'll take you home.

She tucks Basil up under a blanket. Bertie follows her out. He suddenly runs back to Basil.

Bertie   *(softly)* That was the best birthday I ever had! Thank you.

He gives the old scoundrel a kiss and a hug. Basil mumbles in his sleep and rolls over. Bertie runs off.

Scene 11

Bertie's home

Mum is sitting in front of the television, eating chocolates. Bertie enters.

Mum	Oh, hello Bertie, I'd forgotten you were out. Did you remember to buy plenty of washing-up liquid? There's loads of plates in the sink all ready for you.
Bertie	There's liquid in the cupboard.
Mum	Is there? I forgot to look. Where are you going?

He runs back to the door and waves.

	Goodbye!
Mum	Who was that? Not one of your grubby friends, I hope?
Bertie	No. She was … an angel.
Mum	What are you talking about? It's time for bed – but make me a cup of tea first.
Bertie	Yes, Mum.
Mum	And as it's Saturday tomorrow, don't forget you've got to get up early to do the weekend shopping.
Bertie	Yes, Mum.

Scene 12

Hampton Court maze, the next day

Bertie is by the yew hedge in the maze, talking to the audience.

Bertie   I caught the bus back here because I couldn't wait to see Uncle Basil again. I paid my entrance fee, took the path round to the right, then the first sharp left, the next right, then I took the five paces forward and stopped.

Bertie tugs at the hedge.

I grabbed the yew bush and tried to move it, but it stuck fast. So I tried the bushes to the left and the bushes to the right. I couldn't move them. They looked as if they had been growing there for years. I've spent all morning trying to find Uncle Basil's secret hideaway and now I'm beginning to think that I imagined everything. I'm even wondering if Uncle Basil ever existed …

Bertie looks back at the yew hedge, then leaves.

Scene 13

Bertie's home – a few weeks later

Bertie mopes round the house. Mail drops through the letter box and he bends to pick it up.

Bertie   It's a letter for me! It's got a strange postmark and big coloured stamps plastered all over it!

He opens the letter. A folded photograph drops out.

Basil   *(off)* Dear Bertie, I've been missing you very much. I'm having the most wonderful time and wish you were here.

Bertie sticks the large photograph on the wall. It shows Basil lying in a hammock between two palm trees.

Bertie   *(reads)* … I'm sending you these two tickets, one for you and one for Angela, so you can come and visit me here …

Basil   *(off)* You see, I found it. Happiness is not too hard to find, if you know where to look …

Bertie   *(reads)* So remember to ask your Mum
if you can come – I hope she says yes –
and then you and Angela can both join
me here, in this wonderful place called
… Euphemia.

*Bertie stares at the tickets in wonderment, then
runs to the foot of the stairs.*

Mum!